Ships

FRANK KNIGHT

CROWELL-COLLIER PRESS

Library of Congress Catalog Card Number: 70–124418

The Macmillan Company
866 Third Avenue
New York, New York 10022

Printed in Great Britain

First Printing

1   Up on its legs! A U.S. Navy 'hydrofoil' boat, jet propelled. At speed its light hull rises so that only its aerofoil-shaped 'feet' remain in the water, thus reducing friction.

Ships of the Nuclear Age

In 1958 American sailors made a voyage of which men had been dreaming, and trying and failing, for more than four hundred years. In a nuclear-powered submarine, the *Nautilus*, they cruised from the Pacific Ocean into the Atlantic by way of the North Pole.

Away back in the sixteenth century, when Queen Elizabeth I was still a little girl and Francis Drake was unborn, men were saying that such a voyage ought to be possible. So some men tried, and others went on trying through the ages, striving desperately to find a passage for their little wooden sailing ships through the solid Polar ice. And of course they failed because no such passage, due north between ocean and ocean, existed.

But in 1958 the submarine *Nautilus* did succeed because she went *under* the ice, not through it. And her sister-ship *Skate* capped the achievement by exploring almost the whole of the frozen Arctic Ocean beneath the ice. She even crashed her way through the surface ice here and there, where her television cameras indicated a thin patch. And at the North Pole itself, in the darkness of the Arctic winter, her crew held a funeral service for and scattered the ashes of the explorer Sir

2 Ice-breaking tanker *Manhattan*. The largest merchant ship ever to fly the American flag, this was the first surface vessel to navigate the fabled Northwest Passage.

Hubert Wilkins, who a generation earlier, in 1931, had tried and failed to make just such a voyage under the ice in another submarine called *Nautilus*.

Why did the later *Nautilus* succeed where the early one had failed? Chiefly, because the later ship was nuclear-powered, whereas the earlier craft had only diesel engines and electric motors.

The main weakness of the submarine has always been that beneath the surface it is cut off from supplies of air. Yet both its crew and its engines – if these are of normal type – need oxygen. And most engines produce killing exhaust fumes which must be got rid of.

So most of the older submarines had two sets of machinery; a diesel engine for cruising on the surface and charging batteries, and electric motors, which do not discharge poisonous fumes, for running under water. But none of these older boats could remain submerged for long. Sooner or later, with their batteries

3

flat, they had to come to the surface to re-charge. And that was when enemy ships or aircraft could see and sink them. Germany alone, in two world wars, lost many hundreds of submarines as they were recharging their batteries on the surface.

It is true that in the Second World War the Germans invented a very efficient combined breathing and exhaust tube for submarines, the *schnorkel*, by means of which a diesel engine

4 Experimental steam-driven submarine of 1879. Named *Resurgam*, 'I shall arise again', it sank during trials and did not rise again.

3 U.S. Navy nuclear submarine *Nautilus*. In 1958 this vessel cruised from Pacific to Atlantic under the Arctic ice.

could be run under water and the ship remain submerged for many days. In fact in 1945 one German submarine equipped with this appara-tus cruised under water all the way to South America and did not come to the surface for two whole months!

Yet even the *schnorkel* had one big dis-advantage. Its breathing end could be seen trailing along the surface of the sea, a fatal give-away for a submarine which wished to remain hidden. And of course the *schnorkel* could not be used beneath a frozen sea. It could not breathe through ice.

Other ideas have been tried, or at least pro-posed. There have been steam submarines with boilers heated by chemical means, or in which high-pressure steam was raised on the surface and then stored for use under water, and there have been submarines driven by compressed air. But the nuclear submarine has made all these obsolete.

In a nuclear submarine a reactor, fed by minute quantities of uranium, creates great heat without consuming oxygen. This heat is used to generate steam, and the steam drives turbine engines. Thus nuclear power, in the end, revives the despised steam engine which not long ago looked as though it might vanish for ever.

A nuclear submarine has no need to breathe, for sufficient oxygen for its crew can be manufactured or stored for long periods. Moreover, its uranium fuel lasts so long that it can cruise for many months, either on the surface or below it at will, without ever going into port.

Then why is not nuclear power more generally used? Why, in the main, is it thought suitable only for submarines? Why not use it in all ships?

The answer is of course that it is fantastically expensive. Surface ships *can* be given nuclear power. In 1959 America demonstrated that by building the *Savannah*, a nuclear-powered passenger and cargo ship. But she cost forty million dollars, which is about four times the cost of a normal ship of her size, and in operation she has proved far too expensive ever to be run at a profit. With warships, whether sub-

5 A German U-boat of the Second World War. By using such submarines to sink millions of tons of allied shipping Germany attempted to starve her enemies out.

marines or surface vessels, cost is not the most important factor. But merchant ships have to earn their keep. Russia has a nuclear-powered icebreaker, the *Lenin*, but it is doubtful whether she can be called anything but an expensive experiment.

So, before switching its merchant fleets into the nuclear age, the world awaits the discovery of a much cheaper form of nuclear power. And by the time that comes, if it does, the merchant ship may be ready for another and even bigger change. It may be ready to abandon the surface of the sea for the depths beneath.

6 A hovercraft. Not really a ship at all because it rides on a cushion of air just above the surface of the sea. It can also travel over land.

For submarine voyaging has taught us that the depths of the ocean are untroubled by waves, storms or even currents. Beneath the surface a ship may travel at a higher speed – constantly, without effort, and therefore economically – than she can on the surface. And ice, that great danger and barrier on many routes, need not trouble the submarine at all. So the cargo ship of the future may well be a streamlined, torpedo-shaped hull shooting through

7 American nuclear-powered cargo ship *Savannah*, named after an early steamship which crossed the Atlantic in 1819 – *see pages 39, 40.*

the depths at higher speeds than any present-day ship can achieve, and the broad surface of the Atlantic may be once again as empty as it was before Columbus discovered the West Indies. As to passengers, they will all fly, as many of them do today.

One other possible ship of the future needs to be mentioned, and this is the hovercraft. Strictly speaking, of course, it is not a ship at all because it does not float, but rides just above the surface of the water on a cushion of air. That is why it can continue its journey on to dry land, and why it is such a useful vehicle in shallow river estuaries or swamp country. Moreover, because it does not have to overcome the resistance of water, it can travel at high speeds. Its weakness, however, is that it does need a reasonably smooth surface beneath it. Whether big hovercraft will ever be built which can carry heavy loads over rough seas remains to be seen. And, because it is not really a ship at all, we can leave its future to the future and pass on to the real ships of the present day – the ships we can see in every port and on every waterway.

8 Russian nuclear-powered ice-breaker *Lenin* at work. Nuclear-powered ships are extremely expensive to build and to operate.

6

The Cargo Ship - the Present Day

The business of most ships is to carry cargo. We hear a lot about warships and luxury liners, but the most important ship in the world is the humble cargo-carrier which seldom gets into the news or makes history.

Half a century ago Rudyard Kipling wrote in verse:

Oh, where are you going to, all you big steamers,
With England's own coal up and down the salt seas?
We are going to fetch you your bread and your
butter,
Your beef, pork and mutton, eggs, apples and
cheese.

For the bread that you eat and the biscuits you
nibble,
The sweets that you suck and the joints that you
carve,
They are brought to you daily by all us big steamers,
And if anyone hinders our coming you starve.

Not so many steamers carry or burn coal now, but in other ways the words are still true. All those things and many, many more are being carried daily, night and day, by ships on every sea. And if anything does happen to prevent them, such as a war or other disaster, people may starve.

The chief difference since the words were written is that the world's trade has increased and more people want more things than ever Rudyard Kipling knew. Even in northern Canada nowadays people eat oranges grown in South America; and in the tropics of South America housewives use refrigerators possibly made in Canada! Both the oranges and the refrigerators have almost certainly been carried by a cargo ship. But not by the same ship or even the same type of ship. For in this modern world of ours so many goods have to be carried by sea, and in such huge quantities, that special types of cargo ship have been developed for the carriage of almost everything.

Consider petroleum, for instance. Not so long ago it provided mainly fuel for lamps. Only small quantities were needed anywhere

9 A typical tramp-steamer for carrying general cargo. Thousands like her were in use all over the world until recent times.

10 More modern than 9 but still looking old-fashioned with its high funnel, a freight-carrier during the Second World War, heavily loaded.

11 A modern cargo liner, the Cunard Line *Scotia*. Note the short stout masts or 'samson' posts topped with bridges for handling cargo gear.

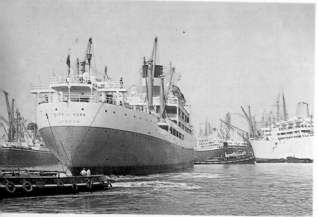

and they could be carried in cans or barrels by ordinary cargo ships. But now every country needs millions of gallons, or even millions of tons, to run its cars, trucks, aircraft, boats, locomotives and machinery of every description. In fact petroleum has become the most important cargo of all and there are more oil tankers afloat than any other kind of ship.

The oil tanker carries petroleum 'in bulk', which means loose, not in barrels or any other kind of container. The ship itself is a tank, or rather a nest of tanks, into which the cargo is pumped from the oil wells or from a refinery or storage tanks. At its destination it is pumped out by the ship's own pumps. Both operations are quick; even very large tankers can be loaded or unloaded in a few hours. And that means the method is cheap; for the longer a ship remains in port loading or discharging cargo the more expensive that cargo becomes. An idle ship costs money in wages, maintenance, harbour dues and so on. That money has to be paid by someone, so it is added to the cost of the cargo.

Also the more oil one ship can carry, the cheaper it is per ton. A ship carrying 50,000 tons can be run with very few more crew, and on very little more fuel, than a ship carrying 20,000 tons. So oil tankers tend to become bigger and bigger as more and more oil is needed everywhere, and the wells produce more and more of it to fill the ships. There are now monster tankers carrying more than 100,000 tons. They are the biggest ships afloat

12 A modern port must be equipped to handle all kinds of cargo. The ship shown has timber stacked on deck and in her holds.

13 Crowded conditions in a big port. Every berth seems to be occupied, yet another ship is being manœuvred by tugs into position somewhere.

14 A grain elevator sucks the cargo out of a ship. But note on this ship the 'goal-post' type mast also used for lifting weights.

15 Without masts or funnel, a coal freighter for river use. It can pass under low bridges.

– far bigger than any warship or great passenger liner.

Many other cargoes can be carried in bulk more cheaply and efficiently than in containers. Most liquids can. There are tankers for carrying liquid chemicals and even for wine. There are 'treacle' tankers which carry sticky molasses which they have to keep hot to prevent it from becoming almost solid and clogging all their valves and pumps. There are tankers for carrying methane gas as a liquid at very low temperatures.

Some ships carry grain in bulk almost like a liquid. It flows into the holds in a golden stream and is sucked out again by giant vacuum cleaners. Coal has been carried in bulk for centuries – Captain Cook's famous exploring ship *Endeavour* was built as a collier away back in 1768 – so have building materials like sand, gravel and clay. Other raw materials like mineral ores are best carried in bulk. Some iron-ore ships are as big as tankers and some can carry oil in tanks on their return journeys.

This is one of the disadvantages of the specialised bulk carrier like the oil tanker. She cannot carry any other type of cargo efficiently, therefore after discharge she has to return empty to a loading port. That is very expensive and wasteful, but so far no general cure has been found for it.

Not all cargoes can be carried in bulk, quite obviously. But a great many classes of goods require very special treatment and care during a voyage; so we have other cargo ships which,

16 The tugboat is the maid-of-all-work in harbours and ports. This one is positioning a ship for entering a lock.

17 Harbours and ports must be kept clear of mud and silt. Here a dredger is working with an attendant tugboat to move it as required.

18 Like super-robots, an army of cranes swing cargo ashore and into barges, trucks or sheds.

19 Salvage vessels equipped with powerful cranes and special lifting gear for recovering lost anchors, sunken wreckage, etc.

9

20   A 'treacle' tanker for carrying molasses in bulk, with special heating equipment to keep it liquid.

21   A diesel-engined coastal cargo-liner. Her job is to carry small consignments of freight from big ports to smaller ones.

though not bulk carriers, are yet specialists in a way.

Those oranges, for instance, and bananas and other kinds of fruit, will have been shipped green so that they can ripen during the voyage and be ready for the market on arrival. But to make sure of that they must be kept at controlled temperatures and well ventilated, or they will go bad. Frozen meat is another cargo requiring special care in refrigerated holds, as do butter and eggs.

Some cargo ships are specially equipped to carry extra-heavy loads like railway locomotives or big machinery. There are timber carriers with doors in their bows through which whole trees – too long to be lowered through any normal hatchway – can be loaded. Then there are the car ferries and train ferries into which vehicles can run under their own power without disturbing their occupants or without having to unload goods from trucks.

22   A giant oil tanker, powered by steam turbines, able to carry 169,000 tons of oil in bulk. The entire ship is a nest of tanks.

Yet there are thousands of things which cannot be carried in bulk, which must be packed in containers of some sort, or of which there are never enough to fill a whole ship. They range from boots and shoes to tractors, from pins and needles to pianos. They form what is called general cargo, so there must always be general cargo ships to carry them. And in some ways this can be the most complicated and difficult cargo of all.

General cargo may arrived in containers of all sizes, types and shapes, in crates, boxes or cartons, in barrels, drums, cans or bags. It has to be stowed so that heavy items do not crush light ones, so that foodstuffs are kept away from things like soap or creosote, and so that leaking liquids will not spoil other goods. Some goods must be kept cool, and you will often see containers marked STOW AWAY FROM BOILERS. Some packages must be stowed one way up, some another; but all must be so stowed that they will not move when the ship rolls. Besides all this, it has to be remembered that, if the ship is calling at several ports, some consignments of cargo will be needed before others. Woe betide the chief officer who

KEY 1 Boiler 2 Force-Draught Fan 3 Auxiliary Machinery 4 Water Inlet Pipe 5 Control Room 6 Oil Fuel Bunker 7 Permanent Ballast Tank 8 Crew Mess 9 Crew Accommodation 10 Master's Accommodation 11 Officers' Accommodation 12 Swimming Pool 13 Navigating Bridge 14 Radar Scanner 15 Fire Hydrant 16 Cargo Hatch and Stand Pipe 17 Structural Arrangement—Centre Cargo Tank 18 Structural Arrangement—Wing Cargo Tank 19 Structural Arrangement—Wing Cargo Tank 20 Hose and Cargo Derrick 21 Breakwater 22 Loading/Discharge Pipelines 23 Bulbous Bow

23　In 1956 this 47,000-ton ship was one of the largest oil tankers afloat. Ten years later there were tankers four times as big.

24　A container carrier. All her cargo is packed in containers of uniform size and shape which stow neatly and safely above and below decks.

discovers that cargo intended for the first port of call is buried deep beneath goods destined for later ports!

In short, general cargo can provide headaches for all concerned – the crew, dock workers, shipowners and shipping agents. It can also be the cause of much wasted time and labour, and even of real danger to the ship if it is badly stowed or breaks loose at sea. So it is not surprising that great efforts have been made through the years to simplify the whole business of carrying it.

One way has been to put ships on regular routes, sailing at scheduled times and calling only at certain specified ports. In other words the cargo ship becomes a cargo liner. Cargo shippers may book space in her perhaps months in advance; but they will be able to tell their agents and customers exactly when the goods will arrive. At the same time shipowners know just what the ship is likely to be carrying on her next voyage, so that she can be prepared for it.

Goods intended for shipment aboard a cargo liner must be delivered to her usual loading port. She will not wait for them; still less will she go out of her way to collect them. And she will carry them only to certain big ports, so that if they have eventually to reach some other port they must be transhipped into smaller vessels. So this system has in turn created smaller cargo liners, coasters or inter-island ships, in many parts of the world. There are regular sailings of such ships, for instance, between Australia and New Zealand or Tasmania, and around the West Indies, and between all the Baltic and Mediterranean countries.

Another development, more recently, has been that of the so-called 'container' service. In this all goods, of whatever kind, *must* be packed in special, standardised metal boxes. These are of certain standard sizes and shapes and can be clipped together like interlocking bricks to form larger units. Ships can then be built or adapted to carry them with a minimum waste of space and every shipowner and chief officer knows exactly how many his ship will carry. In docks lifting and moving gear can be

25　Another modern oil tanker, of 68,000 tons, being helped into her berth by a fleet of tugs at Europort in Holland.

26　A ship specially equipped for laying or repairing submarine telegraph cables. Note the roller-gear at her bows over which cable runs.

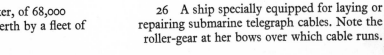

27 This big French tanker, of nearly 70,000 tons, is so automated that she can be operated by one man on the bridge, with nobody in the engineroom.

specially designed to handle them. Road and rail trucks can also be built or adapted specially for them. Thus goods packed in these standard containers need not be unpacked or disturbed between factory and customer, even though the factory be in Chicago and the customer in Timbuktu or Switzerland. This, possibly, will become the most common method of handling general cargo in the future.

But not all cargo ships can be cargo liners or can specialise in one particular kind of cargo. Most shipowners do prefer to keep their ships trading with one particular part of the world, whether it be Australasia, India or the icy region of Hudson Bay. By doing this they can obtain cargoes regularly, while they can build ships of a type most suitable for local conditions or for the kinds of cargo they are most likely to carry. Yet there are still some older ships afloat, and some not so old, which are real tramps – which go anywhere and carry anything and have no regular life at all.

Up to, roughly, the 1920s about half the cargo ships afloat were tramps. Most nations owned them, though by far the majority were British. They were generally quite small, carrying perhaps three or four thousand tons of cargo. They could be seen on every ocean,

28 Mixed cargo. This ship is unloading a large road-tanker. The big logs of timber in the foreground are ready for shipment on board her.

29   A liquid-gas tanker. At very low temperatures the gas is carried from Algeria to Britain for use in ordinary gas-burning appliances.

in big ports and small, or a thousand miles from the sea on some great river like the Amazon.

When a tramp left her home port nobody knew when she would be back. Her crew had probably 'signed on' for three years and they might well be away all of that time. For she might begin by taking Welsh coal to South America, then load raw hides for Spain, then go empty to the Black Sea for wheat, or to Africa for palm nuts or India for jute – to anywhere with anything and from there to anywhere again. The old-type tramp, with her rusty sides and 'salt-caked smoke-stack' was part and parcel of the maritime scene.

That kind of ship and that kind of tramping existence have been squeezed out by modern efficiency. The present-day tramp is likely to be a handy little cargo ship of moderate speed –

say twelve knots – cheap to run and just as capable of going anywhere or carrying anything as her older sister. But she is not so likely to be sent wandering about the world looking for cargoes as in times past. Now her work will be less adventurous and more cut-and-dried, being arranged for her by clerks in some office in London, New York or Hamburg. And she may spend most of her life under charter – hired out – to some big manufacturer or producer who prefers to hire ships rather than own them, or to some owner of big ships who temporarily wants a smaller one. Some modern tramp-owning firms are in fact themselves owned by one or other of the big shipping combines. The small, handy, non-specialised cargo-carrier will always find a use somewhere.

Apart from ships which actually carry cargo, the business of sea trading requires the services of a variety of working ships which do other jobs. For instance, there are the dredgers and icebreakers which keep harbours and narrow waterways open for the cargo ships to

30   A big Italian car-ferry used for conveying cars and their passengers across the Mediterranean.

31   Here the same ship is loading cars on board at Brindisi. Note the doors in square stern through which the vehicles are driven.

pass. There are lightships permanently moored near some sandbank or other obstruction, and there are tenders which keep the lightships, lighthouses and buoys in working order. There are surveying ships constantly checking depths of water and the positions of dangers to navigation, or reporting changes in tides, currents or shoals. There are weather ships far out in the ocean sending information to meteorologists for the compiling of weather forecasts. There are ships whose sole task is to maintain and repair or relay submarine telegraph cables. And of course there are tugs.

Go to any port and you will see the tugs puffing and fussing about, shoving big ships into position or helping them turn tight corners, or bringing strings of barges and lighters to them with cargo. You are less likely to see the really big ocean-going tugs which are ships in their own right; which can take a floating drydock across the world or go to the rescue of a ship in distress in mid-ocean. For many years Holland has been the chief home of these big, immensely powerful vessels, and Dutch seamen have made deep-sea towing a speciality.

And now we must turn to that much more glamorous lady of the seas, the passenger liner.

32 A powerful diesel-engined tugboat working in Adelaide, Australia, where she was built. Note the bluff and cushioned bows for pushing ships into position.

33 A large ocean-going tug towing an oil-rig. Such tugs may be as big as a small cargo ship. Many of the finest are owned in Holland.

34 A dredger at work in Holland on the enclosure of the Zuyder Zee, where vast areas of land have been reclaimed from the sea.

35 A lightship moored on the dangerous Goodwin Sands in the English Channel. Such vessels are used where lighthouses cannot be built.

14

The Atlantic Wonder Ships 1906-66

In the early years of this century a super-ship was built. She was huge and magnificent, a sixth of a mile long, with nine decks piled one above the other and four towering funnels above them. But she was beautiful, sleek as a greyhound, with engines of 50,000 horsepower to drive her across the Atlantic in less time than that ocean had ever been crossed before.

Inside she was like a palace, a ship for princes and millionaires, with a vast ballroom, drawing rooms and dining rooms, a library and a gymnasium, kitchens to produce food

37   A few weeks later, the *Titanic* on her maiden voyage has struck an iceberg and is sinking. More than 1,500 people lost their lives.

36   The *Titanic* setting out on trials in 1912. She was then the biggest and most luxurious passenger vessel afloat and was expected to break all records.

for kings, electrically heated baths and electric lifts.

Proudly her owners named her *Titanic*, for she was the largest ship afloat and the largest ever built anywhere. But very foolishly they also claimed that she was unsinkable, and she was not.

In April 1912 they sent her racing across the Atlantic, out to break the record, with hundreds of stokers deep down in her boiler rooms shovelling coal into her hungry furnaces at the rate of forty tons every hour. And her

38   U.S.S. *United States*, last of the super-luxury Atlantic greyhounds. In 1952 she crossed the ocean at thirty-five knots, a record so far unbeaten.

captain kept her racing on even when his primitive radio warned him that icebergs were near – even when he saw other ships at a standstill because of the drifting ice. It was her first, much-advertised voyage, and she *must* break the record. Besides, she was unsinkable.

Then, just after midnight on 15 April, a man on lookout shouted excitedly that there was a big berg right ahead. The officer on watch threw the helm over and the racing ship swerved; but it was too late. She struck the berg a glancing blow and reeled away.

The few passengers who were still on deck laughed and began playing with chunks of ice

which had cascaded around them. But far down below engineers and stokers were staring in horror at the Atlantic pouring in through a long gash in the ship's hull where the steel plates had been ripped away like paper.

Passengers who had gone to bed were angry when stewards woke them. The *Titanic* in danger of sinking? But that was impossible! But already the poorer passengers in crowded lower-deck cabins were beginning to panic as they found water rising round their feet. Some, who could find their way through the maze of alleyways and staircases, made a rush for the lifeboats, but the ship's officers held them back. There was plenty of time, they were told. Besides, the women and children must go first – and some of the women were not yet dressed!

But there was not plenty of time. Worse still, there were not nearly enough boats to hold everyone. There had been no lifeboat drill so that nobody knew which boat to go to. And many people were still refusing to get into a boat anyway.

39   The celebrated 'Blue Riband of the Atlantic' silver trophy. It is at present held by U.S.S. *United States*, picture above.

Almost suddenly, barely two hours after the lookout man had first shouted, the mighty *Titanic* stood on end and dived. More than 1,500 men, women and children died with her. It was the worst sea disaster in history.

It taught the world one lesson – that no ship is unsinkable. It forced the nations of the world to get together and agree upon safety measures: such things as providing sufficient lifeboats and other life-saving equipment, and as instituting an all-nation ice patrol and advising captains as to the best routes to follow at various times of the year. But it did not stop the building of super-liners.

Nowadays people in a hurry fly across the Atlantic. Only one generation ago they could not; they had to go by ship. But they were just as much in a hurry, so they wanted the fastest ship they could find; and, if they could afford it, the most luxurious ship. In addition to which, the possession of the biggest, fastest and most luxurious ship on the Atlantic was held to give a nation prestige. 'Keeping up with the Joneses' is something nations indulge in just as much as individuals. They do it now with air-liners; before the Second World War they were doing it with ships.

40 Luxury afloat. A full-sized swimming pool aboard a cruising liner. Liner cruises provide super-holidays for many every year.

Speed was the most important factor. If a ship could clip an hour or two off another ship's record she claimed what was called the Blue Riband of the Atlantic. For many years this was a mere title, but in 1935 a British businessman named H. K. Hales presented a real trophy, a valuable silver cup, to be competed for. It is held now by the American liner *United States*.

The most celebrated of these racing Atlantic liners was the old *Mauretania*, built in 1906 for the Cunard Line. She won the Blue Riband in 1909 with an average speed for the ocean

41 For many years the principal maritime nations have maintained 'prestige' ships on the North Atlantic run. This is the *France*, 66,000 tons, leaving New York.

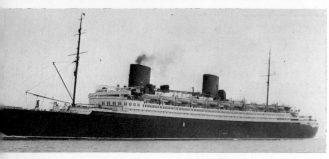

42 The famous Cunard *Mauretania* of 1907. With short breaks she held the record for the Atlantic crossing from 1909 till 1929.

43 The German liner *Bremen* which captured the Blue Riband of the Atlantic in 1929. Compare her raked bow with the straight stem of the *Mauretania*.

44 The German *Europa* which shared the Blue Riband with the *Bremen* and the Italian liner *Rex* between 1929 and 1935.

45 The French liner *Normandie* which created a new record in 1935. Of 86,000 tons, she was then the biggest ship afloat.

46 The Cunard *Queen Mary*, launched in 1934, ended her career as a liner with a voyage round Cape Horn to California in 1968.

crossing of twenty-six knots and held it, with one short break, for more than twenty years. When she was at last broken up, in 1930, people fought to possess scraps of her furnishings and fittings as souvenirs.

In 1929 the German liner *Bremen* captured the record, then for a few years shared it with her sister-ship *Europa* and the Italian liner *Rex*. In 1935 the big French *Normandie* won it, lost it to the British *Queen Mary* a year later, recaptured it, and lost it finally to the *Queen Mary* in 1938. And from then on the *Queen Mary* held it till 1952 when the *United States* pushed the average speed for the crossing up to over thirty-five knots and so made fairly sure of holding the Blue Riband for the remainder of her life.

For the day of the racing wonder-ships is over. Speed is no longer important, either for prestige or for those people who still prefer to cross the Atlantic by sea. Such people now want comfort, or luxury, and safety; and even so they are becoming fewer every year. So the last of the British 'Atlantic ferryboats', as they have been called, have been withdrawn from service as this book is written – the two 'queens', *Queen Mary* and *Queen Elizabeth*. And their newer rival, the *United States*, is being run at well below her maximum speed.

18

Modern Passenger Ships

As fewer people travel by sea, even on long routes, so fewer real passenger ships are built. The modern passenger ship is most often what used to be called an 'intermediate' ship – something between a passenger liner and a cargo ship, carrying passengers and cargo as well. And in many cases the cargo is of more importance than the passengers.

This fits in very well with the development of the cargo liner. A reasonably fast cargo ship making regular scheduled voyages between certain main ports can quite easily carry three or four hundred passengers as well, so cabins and a promenade deck and other facilities are built over her cargo and engine-room space. Frozen meat and fruit ships are very often adapted in this way.

Another factor is that the wealthiest passengers have deserted the sea first and taken to the air. The people who still travel by sea are those who used to take the second and third class cabins and who still want to travel as cheaply as possible. The days when a prince, a millionaire or an Indian grandee would engage a whole suite of rooms and a private deck on some luxury liner have vanished for ever. Now shipowners are glad to cater specially for the once-despised emigrants, for tourists and quite ordinary people taking a holiday.

For this reason many modern passenger ships now carry one class of passengers only. They can still pay more for a large cabin, or for one with its own bathroom, or for one opening directly on to an upper deck. But in such a ship all passengers take their meals in the same saloons, use the same sitting rooms and the same promenade decks, share in the same deck sports, swimming pool and so on. There are no parts of the ship labelled FIRST CLASS PASSENGERS ONLY or SECOND CLASS PASSENGERS NOT ALLOWED ON THIS DECK as there used to be.

Such ships perhaps do not provide super-luxury, but they generally do give super-comfort and a great deal of freedom at very reasonable fares. They are ideal for people who want to combine a holiday with a trip to, say, Australia.

On the other hand some people want the sea holiday, with every possible luxury thrown in, and do not much mind where they go. For them there is the cruising liner. Look in any newspaper and you will see the holiday cruises advertised, from weekend off-shore trips to voyages round the world. For the passenger-ship owner holiday cruising now provides a very useful and profitable sideline.

It has become so profitable that nowadays some of the best and biggest liners leave their regular routes during the winter, when trade is slack, and go holiday cruising to the West Indies or South Seas or Mediterranean. And when a new passenger liner is built its owners are practically certain to keep one eye on its

47 Leisurely life aboard the Cunard *Caronia* during a world cruise. 'Floating hotels' is an apt description of such ships.

suitability for off-season holiday cruising. A liner intended for service between Britain and Canada, for instance, may also have to go to the tropics. The new Cunard liner now being built, as this book is written, to take the place of the two 'queens' on the Atlantic, will have every possible hot-weather luxury besides what is necessary to give comfort on her cold northern run. She will even have iced water piped to every cabin!

49 *Queen Elizabeth 2*, Cunard's new super-liner. She is designed for pleasure-cruising as well as for regular Atlantic service.

48 The *Amazon*, an 'intermediate' or cargo-passenger liner trading to South America. As sea passengers become fewer, cargo becomes more important.

The passenger ship has lost much of her old importance. Generally speaking she is smaller and slower and less grand than some of the great ladies of the past. But she is far from being a thing of the past. So long as people can be found who love the sea, whose chief idea of pleasure is to be on or near the sea, there will be ships ready to accommodate them.

The Warship - the Present Day

The world should be able to do without warships, but seemingly it cannot. Yet many of the warship's old functions have completely disappeared; for instance, it cannot now protect a country from enemy attack, because the attackers fly in far overhead. So the warship, like other kinds of ship, has had to change its form very much in recent years. Also it has had to change much more quickly and radically, because the warship must always be right up to date. If it is old-fashioned it is useless. Therefore hundreds of warships, fantastically expensive to build, go to the scrap-yards without ever having been called upon to fight. Worse still, in these days of leaping scientific progress every warship is out of date in some way by the time her building is completed.

Warships, like passenger ships, tend to

51 Quite small warships may nowadays be very important. This is a guided-missile destroyer, a high-speed laboratory of scientific equipment.

50 A British aircraft carrier of the Second World War. Many early aircraft carriers were converted from existing cruisers or even cargo ships.

become smaller. Great battleships are a thing of the past. Even cruisers, once thought of as small ships, have practically disappeared. The only really big warships still in regular use are aircraft carriers, and they are not likely to last many more years.

The big warship is too vulnerable. She makes a wonderful target from the air, or for the darting little ships or unseen submarines with their torpedoes. She is cumbersome and unable to dodge quickly and there are many places where she cannot go because of the depth of water needed to float her. In the last war the big battleships sometimes proved more

of a nuisance than an asset, for they themselves had to be guarded and nursed by small ships and aircraft which would have been better employed guarding merchant convoys. In one battle in the Mediterranean practically half the Italian fleet had to concentrate on one job only – to get the monster battleship *Vittorio Veneto* safely back to harbour!

Whereas the battleships of the past might be of 40,000 tons, the warships of today seldom exceed 10,000 tons. But the great majority are far smaller than that. They are fast, handy vessels called in some cases after the scouting

53 U.S.S. *Okinawa*, a typical aircraft carrier. The carrier's weapons are its aircraft which can strike at an enemy hundreds of miles away.

52 Anti-submarine, anti-aircraft defence ship. The main task of the modern warship is the protection of merchant convoys, ports and harbours.

sailing ships of Nelson's time – frigates, corvettes and sloops. Other names given them are destroyer-escort, anti-aircraft or submarine-killer ships.

Those names indicate their main purpose – the escort and protection of merchant ships and the keeping open of trade routes. The attackers are submarines and aircraft; these small ships are the defenders.

Most of these vessels are of less than 1,500 tons displacement. Considerably bigger, up to 7,000 tons, are the destroyers – once the small fry of any fleet but now the big ships! They are

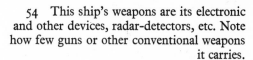

likely to be from 300 to 500 feet long, to have speeds up to forty knots, and to be equipped with every kind of weapon, including guns, torpedoes and guided missiles. Some of the largest United States destroyers have nuclear-powered engines, but the majority, of all nations, have normal oil-fired boilers to drive their steam turbines.

Mines are another weapon much used against merchant ships, so some warships are equipped for mine-laying and others for mine-sweeping. Most of these are not fighting ships, however; the sweepers in particular are more like fishing trawlers.

Another common use for the warship today is that of covering landings by soldiers. The landing craft themselves are scarcely warships, though some are lightly armed and some are quite big ships. A tank landing craft, for

54   This ship's weapons are its electronic and other devices, radar-detectors, etc. Note how few guns or other conventional weapons it carries.

instance, may be of 7,000–8,000 tons. But a special type of warship has been evolved to protect landing craft, called in America a 'bob-tailed' cruiser. It is of about 1,500 tons, has anti-aircraft and other light weapons, and can navigate very close to a beach.

Most modern navies have numerous other types of small craft – coastal patrol vessels, fishery protection ships, high-speed motor torpedo-boats, surveying vessels, submarine and aircraft rescue and repair ships and so on. But on the whole navies of surface ships are shrinking. If another major war should come it will be fought out above and below the surface.

55   A British frigate on special mission. The royal standard flying at the masthead indicates the presence of the sovereign on board.

56   Converted from a landing craft; this vessel can operate in very shallow water to cover troop landings etc.

Times of Change 1900-1950

We need not go back many years to discover a world very different from our own. Many people still living can remember when there were no motor cars or aeroplanes and when working sailing ships were almost as common as steamers. In our world change is rapid and we take it for granted. Every year there are new inventions and new discoveries. In ten years' time the bright ideas of today may seem absurdly old-fashioned.

Yet for centuries the world jogged along almost without change. In 1492 Christopher Columbus sailed to America in the *Santa Maria*; in 1580 Francis Drake completed his voyage round the world in the *Golden Hind*; in 1768 Captain Cook explored Australia and New Zealand in the *Endeavour*. Those three ships, spanning nearly three centuries, were different from each other only in detail. All were little wooden square-rigged sailing ships about 100 feet long. Columbus could have sailed Drake's flagship; Cook would not have felt lost aboard either of the earlier ships. But

imagine Captain Cook's bewilderment if he were to be put in charge of a nuclear submarine! And that superstitious man Christopher Columbus would have fallen on his knees at sight of the humblest steam tramp.

Sometimes change has been swift, sometimes slow. From 1800 to 1900 was a period of slow development on the whole. The steamboat was invented, was gradually improved and made larger. Steam engines had one cylinder, then two, then three or four. High-pressure boilers increased their efficiency. The screw propeller replaced paddlewheels. Iron and steel hulls replaced wooden ones. The span between the *Victory* and the battleships of the Second World War is one of 125 years only, a comparatively short period in the history of the ship.

Nevertheless, any change took time. Men looked back at the past centuries of little

24

change and mistrusted the new ways. Forty years passed before most navies even began to experiment with steam warships, or with iron hulls. Right to the end of the century many steamers – even warships and big passenger ships – carried masts and spars and sails in case the engines broke down. Even after 1900 some cargo-ship owners refused to have steamers at all, but clung to their old sailing ships.

Yet just at about this time, the turn of the century, a period of rapid change was beginning.

The first sign of it came in 1897, the year of Queen Victoria's Diamond Jubilee, when she

58 *Turbinia*, the first vessel to be powered by a steam turbine. In 1897 she startled the world by racing among the warships gathered for a royal review.

had reigned for sixty years. In honour of that event a great fleet of warships from many nations was assembled off Portsmouth for Her Majesty to review. Then suddenly, a few minutes before the royal yacht was to begin its stately progress, an intruder appeared – a tiny, screaming torpedo-boat type of craft which went darting through the lines and in and out among the waiting ships at the unheard-of speed of thirty knots!

Admirals swore and shook their fists; but they had to take notice, for this little craft, *Turbinia*, could obviously outpace their fastest warships. And so the marine steam-turbine engine, invented by a north-of-England

59 Lord Nelson's *Victory*, sailing wooden battleship of 2,000 tons. The battleship scarcely changed in type for 300 years, from Drake's time to mid-nineteenth century.

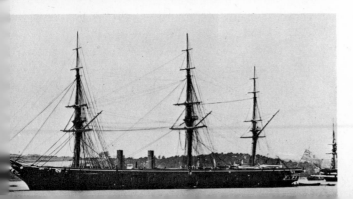

engineer named Charles Parsons who had chosen this startling way of getting publicity, almost immediately made the old piston-type or reciprocating engines seem out-of-date. Within three or four years several nations had turbine-engined destroyers capable of more than thirty knots. In 1907 the record-breaking Atlantic liner *Mauretania* was given turbine engines as was Britain's new super-battleship *Dreadnought*. Charles Parsons had made his point.

Another big change which came in the first quarter of this century was the introduction of oil fuel. Up to the time of the First World War very nearly all steamers burnt coal. The tiny racing *Turbinia* burnt coal. So did even oil tankers carrying whole cargoes of oil in their tanks! For coal was cheap and could be obtained everywhere – there were coaling stations all over the world; but oil was expensive and usually could only be obtained in small quantities.

During the First World War so many cargo ships were sunk that in many places there was a shortage of coal, and it became expensive. Therefore ships trading to oil-producing countries were converted to burn oil; and much coarse black oil which had hitherto been regarded as a waste residue from the refineries was discovered to be quite suitable for burning in ships' furnaces.

Before the end of the war in 1918 many ships were using the new fuel, both warships and merchant vessels. During the 1920s the demand for oil fuel grew so that oil tankers had

60 The *Dreadnought* of 1906 made all other battleships obsolete. Of 20,000 tons, she had ten 12-inch guns and her steam turbines drove her at twenty-one knots.

61 H.M.S. *Inflexible*, a battleship of 1876. She had masts and sails solely for the purpose of exercising her crew to keep them fit!

62 An iron battleship of 1867, with a sailing rig for real use. Note the gun ports, her main armament still being arranged as a broadside.

63 H.M.S. *Warrior* of 1860, the first big all-iron warship, which ended for ever the long era of the 'wooden walls'. Tonnage 9,200, speed fourteen knots.

to be built in their hundreds, and oil depots were established in every big port. On the other hand unwanted coal carriers and storage hulks could be seen abandoned everywhere.

Oil had so many advantages. It could be burnt cleanly, almost without smoke. It could be loaded cleanly through pipelines. It could be carried anywhere in the ship, in double-bottoms and bilges as well as in special bunker tanks. Therefore a ship could carry more of it than of coal and need not put into port for refuelling so often. Above all, it did away with the army of stokers and coal-trimmers so necessary to every big coal-burning ship. The work of sixty men could now be done by six!

65   Steamers, native boats and horse transport at Calcutta in the 1880s. Most of the steamers shown belong to the British India Steam Navigation Co.

64   An early oil tanker, the *Chigwell*. Note her old-fashioned topmasts and strange 'whaleback' stern.

Coaling ship had always been a major operation. The dust from it got everywhere – into the food and into clean clothes packed in drawers. Moreover, in a big ship it might take days and involve the labour of hundreds of men – or even women, in some ports. And then at sea, as the furnaces used it up, so more would have to be carried to the stokeholds, perhaps from the other end of the ship. The burning of coal meant constant labour, constant dust, and clouds of sooty smoke trailing after the ship or settling on her.

At about the same time the first motor ships began to appear – ships with diesel engines

which required no boilers or furnaces or stoke-holds. At first sight they seemed to offer many advantages in the way of space-saving and doing without stokers altogether. But in fact they had disadvantages, too. They needed more skilled engineers to tend them than the simpler steam engines and they were often unreliable. Moreover, they had to use an explosive oil which was far from cheap. So the motor ship has not driven the steamer from the seas as some people thought it would.

As we have already said, the first decades of this century saw the growth and triumph of the big express passenger liner. They also saw the growth and final failure of the big battleship.

67 Many early passenger steamers were extremely graceful. This is the paddle-wheeler *Nyanza* of the P. & O. Line, in about 1870.

66 Another view of the epoch-making *Warrior* of 1860. Of yacht-like shape, she could make thirteen knots under sail alone.

Between 1900 and 1914 Britain and Germany were the great naval rivals. Each strove to build more and better fighting monsters than the other. If one went ahead, as Britain did in 1906 when the famous *Dreadnought* was launched, the other nation sent spies to steal its rival's secrets so that it could go one better. By 1914, when war broke out, Britain and Germany had about forty 'Dreadnoughts' between them. At the battle of Jutland in 1916 some of them hammered each other to pieces and both sides claimed the victory; but in fact it was a useless battle which decided nothing.

Jutland should have taught the nations that the big battleship was practically useless,

but it did not. The United States, Japan, Britain, France, Germany and Italy all went on building the monsters, all competing together. But when the Second World War came in 1939 the great sea battles were nearly all fought by the aircraft flown off from carriers hundreds of miles apart. And the big battleships were nearly all sunk or crippled by the bombs of aircraft or the torpedoes of submarines and small ships. Now there are scarcely any left.

To sum up, then, the first half of the twentieth century was a period of great change – of many and rapid changes. It saw the development of the specialist cargo ship and

68 Wooden steam coastal vessels of about 1840–50. Queen Victoria once travelled to Scotland and back in a similar ship.

the cargo liner and the virtual disappearance of the once ubiquitous tramp steamer. It saw the triumph and decline of the big passenger liner and the passing of the battleship. It saw the change from coal to oil fuel, the introduction of the steam turbine and the diesel engine, of radio and of a host of minor things. It saw the coming of the submarine and its advance from a dangerous toy to a ship of real importance.

Leading up to the twentieth century there was already the transitional period of steam allied to sail, so that the early 1900s also saw the final disappearance of the ocean-going sailing ship after a life of many centuries. And that is what we must look at next.

69 Another graceful steamer, the paddle-wheeler *Leinster*, built in 1860 for the Irish mail service. She had a speed of nearly eighteen knots.

The Windjammers 1870-1920

The change from sailing ships to steamers did not come suddenly. For many years after their invention steamers were both unreliable and expensive. They burnt huge quantities of coal and sometimes had to go hundreds of miles out of their way to get more. Sometimes they ran out of fuel at sea, or burst their boilers or caught fire. Minor breakdowns were too frequent to be counted.

The sailing ship was cheap because she used no fuel. She could make long voyages – from Europe or America to Australia or China, for instance – without having to put in at any port on the way. If she broke down, perhaps when a storm ripped her sails or broke her spars, her own crew could usually get her out of trouble. A broken mast might be mended; but not a steamer's broken connecting rod or propeller shaft. A new mast could be obtained in any port; but not a new boiler.

So for fifty years, roughly from 1820 to 1870, it was the steamer which was fighting to make headway against the sailing ship; and the sailing ship carried most of the world's cargoes. But for the next fifty years, roughly from 1870 to 1920, the sailing ship was losing steadily until as a regular profit-making cargo-carrier she finally vanished. There were a few big sailing ships afloat until the 1950s, but they were mostly boys' training ships or were being run at a loss by sentimental owners who hated to see them withdrawn.

The steamer won the fight because she became more efficient. The sailing ship lost because she must always depend on the wind, and the wind is notoriously fickle. The sailing ship might run out to Australia in sixty days; but she might take six months. She might make a good run across the ocean, then have to wait weeks for a favourable wind to allow her to navigate some narrower waterway such as the English Channel or the passage through the China Sea, or she might not arrive at all.

A sailing ship cannot be handled like a steamer. A sudden change of wind, a swiftly rising storm or an unexpected calm, catching her close to shore or in confined waters, may bring disaster. Hundreds and hundreds of sailing ships, with their cargoes, lie scattered around the Scilly Isles, Cape Horn, Newfoundland, Ushant in France and similar 'black spots'. Very many indeed of those wrecks would not have happened if the ships concerned had possessed engines. In any detailed history of the sailing ship the names of vessels will be followed, one after the other, by such words as *wrecked*, *sunk*, *lost at sea* or just *missing*.

The year 1870 is a good one from which to mark the decline of the sailing ship and the

70   Windjammer – the 2,600-ton steel four-masted barque *Viking*. Such ships, mainly Scandinavian owned, brought Australian wheat home until the 1950s.

71 *Herzogin Cecilie*, another big four-masted barque, three times winner of the 'grain race' home from Australia.

72 Disaster. The *Herzogin Cecilie* wrecked near Salcombe, Devon. Without engines, such ships could not often be saved when driven upon a lee shore.

beginning of the triumph of the steamer. It was the first year after the opening of the Suez Canal.

The opening of the Canal cut thousands of miles off voyages to Australia, India or the Far East. It gave steamers an easy, smooth passage through the Mediterranean and Red Seas with plenty of coaling stations along the route. But it was a very difficult route for sailing ships, involving narrow ways, fitful winds and an expensive tow by steam tugs through the Canal.

The opening of the Panama Canal in 1914 gave a similar tremendous advantage to steamers, for it gave them a relatively calm route from Atlantic to Pacific while sailing ships were forced still to use the stormy way round distant Cape Horn. But by 1914 the sailing ship was dying anyway. In 1870 she was very much alive.

In 1870 the Indian and Far Eastern trades were far more important than those with South America or the Pacific. San Francisco then was still a shanty-town and California as unknown, to most of the world, as the mountains of Peru or the forests of the Amazon. But from India and China came most of the world's luxury

goods – tea, silks and other fine cloths, coffee, pepper and other spices, as well as jute and hemp for rope-making, minerals like copper and tin and a host of other valuable or not so valuable materials. And, of course, there was a great going to and fro of passengers, including wealthy merchants, government officials and soldiers, for Britain then ruled India, Holland ruled the East Indies, France much of Indo-China, with other western nations staking rival claims.

Almost immediately after the opening of the Suez Canal the sailing ship lost most of this first-class trade. Who wanted to make the long, uncertain and uncomfortable voyage round the Cape of Good Hope when he could travel more swiftly and safely in a steamer going through the Canal? Who would send a cargo like tea – which everybody said was ruined by a long sea voyage – in a sailing ship taking four or six months when it could be carried in a steamer in half the time?

The sailing ship was forced to concentrate on the less valuable, less well-paying freight. The fast tea-clippers turned to Australian wool, which was becoming important and which was usually wanted in a hurry – for the

31

73 One of the largest sailing ships ever built, the steel five-masted barque *France*. She was abandoned at sea and sank in 1901.

first cargoes of a new season's clip to reach the market could fetch a high price. And on the Australian run, for a while, a fast sailing ship could still keep pace with a steamer. There were even many passengers on that route who preferred to travel by sailing ship. Fast sailing ships with good passenger accommodation were being built for the Australian trade until the 1890s.

Then that trade, too, fell to the faster and more efficient steamers. Sailing ships had to be content with such cargoes as nobody wanted in a hurry but everybody wanted carried cheaply – coal, minerals, fertilisers, raw hides, timber and so on.

Cheapness became all-important and most sailing-ship owners did everything they could to achieve it. The old fast clippers had their masts and sail area reduced so that they could be handled by fewer men. In many ships boys took the place of men; some big sailing ships carried forty or fifty unpaid apprentices and only eight or ten paid seamen. But the wages of

74 A clipper of 1864. For more than 300 years the 'ship' rig, three-masted with square sails on all three, was standard for ocean-going vessels.

the paid men *per month* were no more than a skilled worker might earn *per day* now, while their working and living conditions and food were so bad that no government would dare permit them today. Imagine existing for weeks during the long battle against Cape Horn storms, with wet bunks and wet clothes, without heating or lamps of any sort below decks, eating nothing but a hash of salt meat and half-rotten ships' biscuit day after day, and that usually stone-cold. Imagine, with all that,

75 A Blackwall 'frigate'. These smart passenger ships took over the trade of the old East India Company in the 1850s and 1860s.

having to work at all hours of the day and night, snatching sleep in short naps and as often as not having those interrupted by the cry 'All hands on deck!' And then imagine the kind of work it was, often high above the deck clawing at wet canvas with frozen fingers and clinging for life to a swaying, dancing network of sticks and string. No wonder the seamen, as well as the passengers and cargo owners, turned to the steamer and abandoned the sailing ship!

But sailing ships continued to be built. To

76 *Taeping*, one of the fastest China tea clippers. In 1866 she won the tea race home from China, beating *Ariel* by twenty minutes after ninety-nine days.

77 A tower of sail. The steel four-masted barque *Pamir*, one of the last sailing ships in the Australian grain trade.

secure cheapness they had to be bigger, to carry more cargo on each voyage. Whereas once few sailing ships exceeded 1,000 tons – the fast clippers were nearly all smaller than that – in the 1890s they were built of 3, 4 or 5,000 tons. Their shape had changed, too, The fine lines of the old ships, built for speed, were no longer wanted. The new ships had to be almost square in section, with straight sides and nearly flat bottoms. 'Built by the mile and cut off by the yard,' said the old sailors of them scornfully. And the same men called them 'wind-jammers', because they *jammed* themselves into the wind, however hard it blew, instead of skilfully and sensitively *feeling* their way through its vagaries as the old-time clippers had done.

Yet the best of the new ships were beautiful and impressive in their way. Most were built of steel. Some had steel masts and yards and even some steel-wire rigging. Many had four masts instead of the three which had once been universal. Some had five masts, like the German *Preussen* and *Maria Rickmers* and the French *France*. The American schooner

78 The 'sticks and string' of a clipper. Above her lower sails or 'courses' she sets upper and lower topsails, topgallants, royals and skysails.

THE CALIPH
SCALE- ⅛ · 1 FOOT.

Thomas W. Lawson even had seven, named, so it was said, after the seven days of the week because nobody could invent, or remember, proper technical names for them!

But the old sailors were right in one way. These big sailing ships were brutes to handle. If they did not kill their crews by other means, they drowned them. The *Preussen* was wrecked; the *Maria Rickmers* just vanished; the *France* had to be abandoned at sea in a sinking con-

79 Sailing tramp ship. Work-worn and with patched sails. The three-masted barque rig shown was easier to handle than the full 'ship' rig.

dition; the *Thomas W. Lawson* capsized near the Scilly Isles and drowned all her crew except one man. The list could be added to almost endlessly. Few of these big windjammers ever reached the breakers' yards.

So the steamer won in the end, though it took her just about a hundred years to do it. And now we must look at those hundred years and see how the steamer grew from the experimental stage to maturity.

80 A forest of masts at Melbourne, Australia, in 1874. The long ocean run to Australia enabled sail to hold off steam competition for many years.

The Steamer Grows up 1800-1900

In 1766-9 James Watt of Glasgow, improving upon earlier inventions, produced the first workable small steam engine. And almost immediately other inventors set to work to make the steam engine propel a boat. After all, men had been dreaming for centuries of ships which would be independent of the wind, but so far the only practicable solution had seemed

did succeed in making a boat move, slowly, by means of steam-driven oars; but people only laughed, and poor Fitch committed suicide. In the same year James Rumsay of Maryland had some success with another idea – propelling a boat by means of a jet of water pumped out astern. But few people showed much interest in that either.

81 *Charlotte Dundas*, stern paddlewheel tugboat of 1801, the first steamer to work for its living anywhere in the world.

to be the rowing galley propelled by scores of men labouring at huge oars.

Because of that these early inventors could not get the idea of oars out of their heads. In France the Marquis de Jouffroy made a steamboat as early as 1776; but its weird arrangement of flapping paddles were a complete failure. In 1787 John Fitch of Philadelphia

In the meantime the Marquis de Jouffroy had hit upon a much better solution to the problem – the paddlewheel. In 1783-4 he had a boat with twin paddles running quite well on the River Saône, so it is he who really deserves the title 'inventor' of the steamboat, if anyone does. Yet even so, people only jeered at him, and told him he was mad to try 'to make fire and water agree'. And soon after that the French Revolution put a stop to his activities, for he was an aristocrat and had to leave France to save his life.

The first steamboat really to work for its living, however, was the little tugboat *Charlotte Dundas*, which a Scottish inventor named William Symington had towing barges along the Forth and Clyde Canal in 1801–2. Then it had to be stopped because the wash from its single stern paddlewheel was damaging the banks of the canal.

By that time Europe was too busy with the Napoleonic Wars to bother much with steam-

82 Mississippi river steamboat. The great American rivers allowed steamers to be developed in better conditions than the open sea.

boats, so progress was left to the Americans. In 1804 one American inventor, John Stevens, leapt right ahead of all others by building a boat with twin *screw* propellers which made a speed of eight knots. But then, for some unknown reason, he dropped this highly efficient method of propulsion and gave his next vessel twin side paddlewheels.

His great rival was Robert Fulton, who in 1807 put his famous *Clermont* to work on the

83 Mississippi river steamers refuelling. They burnt wood (note the pile ready in the foreground) and belched sparks and flames.

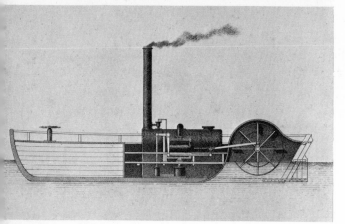

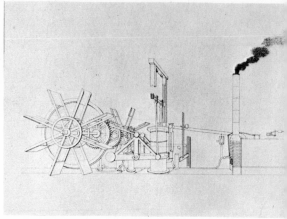

84 A steam-oared boat at Philadelphia in 1787. It moved, but only just. Its inventor, John Fitch, committed suicide when people jeered at him.

85 Robert Fulton's famous *Clermont* of 1807 steaming between New York and Albany. She terrified farmers along the river banks.

86 Machinery of the Scottish tug *Charlotte Dundas*. Robert Fulton studied this boat before building his successful *Clermont*.

87 Machinery of Fulton's *Clermont*. The engine was made in England by Boulton and Watt. It propelled the ship at nearly five knots.

Hudson River, carrying both passengers and freight. She is often claimed to be the first really successful American steamboat. But within a few days Stevens had a similar boat, the *Phoenix*, trading regularly on the Delaware, where she continued running for six years. And she had already made the sea voyage from New York to Philadelphia, so she was certainly the first American steamboat to go to sea and probably the first in the world.

Of course the big American rivers provided an ideal testing ground for the steamer, and ideal trading routes once the testing time was over. There were no railways and almost no roads. Scores of townships were growing along the rivers and the new steamers came to serve

them. Passengers flocked to them because they provided the only efficient means of travel. Cargo was brought to them from farms and plantations a hundred miles or more away. Trade boomed and more and more steamers were built. Skippers and owners became jealous rivals. There was racing between boats which sometimes led to burst boilers and collisions. At one time a price-war between rival owners of steamboats on the Hudson led to the passenger fare between New York and Albany, 145 miles, being cut to $12\frac{1}{2}$ cents! Other owners on this route tried to attract passengers by equipping their vessels with a kind of steam organ called a 'calliope', which played pop music of the period on a dozen or so steam whistles and could be heard several miles away. But it was on the Mississippi that rivalry really mounted to fever-pitch. In the 1830s at least two big Mississippi steamers blew up with the loss of hundreds of lives. But when the racing monsters took to ramming each other deliberately, as the *Pioneer* and *Ontario* did in 1838, killing some passengers in the process, people rebelled and the racing was stopped.

By comparison with the American boom, progress in Europe seems slow. Half a dozen steamers were running regularly on American rivers by the time Henry Bell, a Glasgow hotel owner, put into commission the pioneer British steamboat, the tiny *Comet*, in 1812. But Europe could not provide the steamboat with anything like the big American waterways in which to get over their teething troubles. In Europe the steamer, to be of any use, had to be a sturdy sea-going ship. Nevertheless, progress was rapid once a start had been made.

The little *Comet*, only forty feet long, carried passengers down the Clyde and sometimes round the dangerous Scottish coast. She had no steam organ to attract passengers, but she did have a bagpiper! Then in 1815 another Scottish-built boat, the *Thames*, made a hazardous voyage from the Clyde to the Thames by way of Land's End. On the Thames she became the first steamer to run regular trips between London and Margate – a popular passenger service to this day. Only a year later, in 1816, the famous steamer service to Ireland from Holyhead was opened by the little *Hibernia*, of 112 tons. And soon after that steamers were plying between England and France, between London and Edinburgh and across the North Sea to Holland and Germany.

Just as in America, competition in these early days was furious and foolish. One company actually carried passengers to Ireland for nothing for a while, and a rival concern capped

that by offering them free bread and beer as well!

Then men began to think about crossing the Atlantic by steam power. If steamers could cross the Irish Sea or make long sea voyages along the Atlantic coast of the United States, why should they not cross the Western Ocean itself? Yet to some men it seemed such a foolish dream that one Member of Parliament offered publicly to eat his hat if it ever came to pass. As to whether he did eat it or not there is no record.

In fact a steamer crossed the Atlantic as early as 1819 – the famous *Savannah*. But she was a full-rigged sailing ship of 350 tons with a small auxiliary steam engine, and she used that engine only for 80 hours during the voyage, which lasted 29½ days in all. So this can scarcely be called the first crossing under steam power. Nor did the *Savannah* long remain a steamer, for her engine was removed from her a few months later. If it had not been, perhaps it would have saved her from being wrecked on Long Island in 1822.

Another ship which sailed and steamed her way across was the Canadian *Royal William* in

88   The first successful passenger steamer in Europe, Henry Bell's *Comet* on the Clyde. Music was provided on board by a bagpiper!

89   The celebrated Mississippi river steamers *Robert E. Lee* and *Natchez* racing from New Orleans to St Louis. The *Robert E. Lee* won.

90 The *Savannah*, first steamer to cross the Atlantic, in 1819, but did most of the journey under sail. Later her engine was removed altogether.

1833. Later she became a Spanish warship and was the first steamer ever to fire a gun in war. Her Atlantic journey took thirty-eight days – possibly a slower trip than if she had sailed all the way!

Five years after that, however, the Atlantic really was conquered by steam power, and the event was quite as thrilling as anyone could have wished. Two companies decided to 'have a go' at the same time, one of them being the Great Western Railway Company whose chief engineer, Isambard Brunel, had advised his employers to extend their new line all the way to New York. They took his advice and he built for them the *Great Western* of 1,320 tons and 236 feet long, with engines of 750 h.p.

Meanwhile a rival concern, the Transatlantic Company, realised that they could not build a ship in time, so they hired the little *Sirius*, of 703 tons, from an Irish packet company. So for that ship the great adventure came most unexpectedly. And the big race was on. Could the little ship beat the big fellow? Could the little *Sirius* make the crossing at all?

The *Sirius* steamed down the Thames on 28 March and passed the *Great Western*, which was still running trials. She also passed a fast American sailing packet, the *Quebec*, and a good many people laid bets on the sailing ship beating both steamers. But the *Sirius* was still well ahead when on 4 April she left Ireland behind after loading just as much coal as she could carry, together with mail and passengers.

Her captain, Lieutenant Roberts R.N., might have worried less if he had known of the troubles of the *Great Western*. As she was leaving the Thames she caught fire and the engine-room crew fled to the deck, leaving the engines running. Then she ran on to a sandbank and lay there while her crew put out the

91 Frozen in at Boston, Massachusetts, the first Cunarder, *Britannia*. To help her maintain schedule the citizens turned out to clear a passage for her.

92 *Great Western*, the first steamer specially built for the Atlantic 'ferry'. From 1837 to 1846 she made sixty-four crossings.

fire. By the time she finally commenced her voyage, from Bristol, the *Sirius* was about four days ahead.

But the *Sirius* had her troubles too. After she had been punching into head gales for several days, and was in danger of running short of fuel, her crew showed signs of mutiny. Lieutenant Roberts had to threaten them with a pistol to get them back to work. However, they did go back, and the *Sirius* ploughed bravely on, and at ten o'clock at night on 22 April she reached New York, where almost the entire population turned out to welcome her. And then, barely were they in their beds after a hectic night when in came the *Great Western*! But nobody noticed at all when the fast sailing packet *Quebec* arrived many days later.

So steamers *could* cross the Atlantic and could even maintain a regular service across it, as Mr Samuel Cunard and his partners proved when in 1840 they founded the famous Cunard Line with three little wooden paddle steamers, *Britannia*, *Arcadia* and *Columbia*. They could beat the sailing ships on average speed and reliability, making a regular eight or nine knots and taking fourteen days for the passage from Liverpool to Halifax and Boston. They were much safer; but they were scarcely more comfortable, as Charles Dickens discovered when he crossed to Halifax in the *Britannia* in 1842.

Head wind or not, the brave *Britannia* made that crossing in eleven days and returned to Liverpool in ten. But Charles Dickens had had enough of her. He went home by sailing ship.

It is amusing to think that the *Britannia*, the first Cunarder, could easily have been carried on deck by one of her big descendants, such as the *Queen Elizabeth*.

93 New York without skyscrapers, viewed from Brooklyn. Note the steam ferries and river steamers, the waterside in background thick with masts. About 1840.

Iron Ships

Wooden steamers were never very satisfactory. The weight of their engines, boilers and fuel was more than wooden hulls could stand, while the thumping and pounding of pistons, cranks and huge paddlewheels shook them to pieces. There was also a big risk of fire with roaring furnaces being stoked only feet away from wooden planking.

Wood was not even very satisfactory for big sailing ships. If they were not built strongly enough they 'hogged' – which means their ends dropped so that they became arch-backed – or they 'sagged', which means their middles dropped. Or else knees, brackets and joints worked loose, planking came apart, and the ship quite literally did fall to pieces. Yet to get the necessary strength timbers had to be huge and enormously heavy. So very big wooden ships were never possible. Nelson's *Victory* was only 200 feet long, and the biggest all-wooden sailing ship ever built, the American clipper *Great Republic*, measured only 325 feet. The largest wooden steamers did not exceed 300 feet.

Besides, good timber was becoming scarce. In Europe naval officials searched desperately for oak trees. Admiral Collingwood, Nelson's second-in-command at Trafalgar, was so worried that he used to carry acorns in his pocket and plant them on any vacant land. In Canada and the United States vast forests were felled to meet the rush of shipbuilding. Nova Scotia, a land covered with trees at the beginning of the nineteenth century, was stripped almost bare to build the famous 'Bluenose' ships. In 1870 or thereabouts it was estimated that more than half of all sailing ships flying the British flag were of Nova Scotia build! In New Zealand, too, the great kauri pines and other trees were ruthlessly felled.

There was tremendous opposition to the use of iron. How could iron float? Besides, it would crack, bend, twist, rust away and do all

94 S.S. *Great Britain*, built 1843, first all-iron Atlantic liner. She is still in existence to this day, beached in the Falkland Islands.

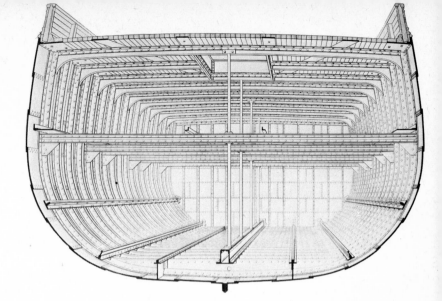

95   Section showing
framing of monster iron
steamer *Great Eastern*.
Built in 1857, her
advanced design was many
years ahead of its time.

kinds of unpleasant things. And it was much
heavier even than oak.

But the engineers and builders went on with
their experiments and by 1840 or thereabouts
had proved their case. Iron could be used, not
only for knees and brackets and frames, but
even for shell plating. It was cheaper than
wood. It was even lighter because iron com-
ponents could be so much less massive than
wood – an iron ship was only two-thirds the
weight of a wooden ship of the same size. It
was stronger than wood, as was demonstrated
in 1834 when the little iron steamer *Garry
Owen* ran on to rocks in a storm in company
with several wooden vessels. The wooden ships
were soon knocked to pieces; the *Garry Owen*
came off with a few dents.

Above all, really big ships could be built of
iron. In 1843 the great engineer Isambard
Brunel built the *Great Britain* for the Atlantic
service, of 3,270 tons and 322 feet long. *The
Times* newspaper described her as 'a stupen-
dous steamship of unparalleled vastness'! But
in 1857 Brunel astonished the world with a
monster of really 'unparalleled vastness' – the
Great Eastern. Of 32,000 tons and 690 feet
long, she had five funnels and six masts,
paddlewheels and a screw propeller as well,
and could carry 4,000 passengers or 10,000
troops. On her trial trip she made fourteen-
and-a-half knots.

The *Great Eastern* proved that ships of
almost any size could be built of iron. In other
ways she was a failure, and the only useful job
she ever did was to lay the first telegraph cable
across the Atlantic. Brunel had gone ahead of
his age. The world was not yet ready for such
monster ships.

Almost the last people to be persuaded that
iron was better than wood were the old admirals
and naval officials of the world. They were
building wooden warships until well into the
1860s, although by that time they were encas-
ing them in iron armour – thus, of course,
increasing their weight to absurdity. The
first all-iron warship in the world was the
British *Warrior* of 1860. The first in America
was the famous little two-gun *Monitor* which
in 1862 fought a great duel in Hampton Roads
with the Confederate iron-armoured frigate
Merrimac – the first battle of ironclads in
history.

Then in the 1870s an even better material,
steel, lighter and stronger than iron, was
introduced. Of course the world had known
about steel for centuries, especially for sword-
blades and knives; but not until the 1870s was
any means found of producing it cheaply and
in great quantities. When it came it soon swept
the board. By 1880 merchant steamers and
warships and even sailing ships were all being
built of steel.

Screw versus Paddle

Nobody suddenly invented the screw propeller. The idea had been talked about for at least fifty years before John Stevens tried it out with a steam engine in 1804. Men went on talking about it and experimenting with it for years after that. The trouble was that the paddlewheel *looked* efficient and could be made to push steamers along at quite a fair speed – in smooth water. But sailors and engineers knew how it wasted power with its furious churning and how when a ship rolled one paddle was as often as not out of the water altogether.

Builders of warships were particularly interested in the screw propeller. Paddles were far too vulnerable; they could be seen and shot at and put out of action. But the screw was smaller and out of sight and therefore much safer. What few people could believe was that a tiny screw might actually be more powerful than two massive paddlewheels. So in 1843 the British naval authorities tied two vessels together, stern to stern, and set them pulling against each other. Both were of similar size and engine-power; one, the *Alecto*, had paddles; the other, the *Rattler*, had a single screw. And to the surprise of most people the screw boat towed the paddlewheeler astern at two-and-a-half knots with paddles thrashing helplessly.

96 The huge *Great Eastern*, 690 feet long and of 32,000 tons, had paddles, screws and sails on six masts as well. But she was a monster failure.

97 The first battle of ironclads, between the two-gun turret ship *Monitor* and the armoured frigate *Merrimac*. American Civil War, 1862.

98 *Great Eastern* passing one of the last wooden battleships. She laid the first Atlantic cable, the only useful task of her lifetime.

99 Screw or paddle? Two near-identical steamers fight it out. In the event the screw-driven *Rattler* towed the paddle-wheeler *Alecto* astern at two and a half knots.

After this most builders adopted the screw propeller and paddlewheels went out of fashion except for river and harbour steamers.

But at the same time the steam engine itself had to be adapted, because the screw propeller needed a much faster-revving engine than the old slow pump-type machines which had suited heavy and ponderous paddlewheels. So very soon engineers were producing small, efficient, fast-running engines with two, three or four cylinders and using steam from high-pressure boilers. And right at the end of the nineteenth century, as has been said already, the steam turbine arrived.

The change from wood to iron and then from iron to steel, and the change from paddles to screw propellers, came fairly quickly. It took much longer for people to realise that steamers no longer needed sails to help them along or get them out of trouble.

Most steamers carried massive yards and a locker full of sails until the end of the nineteenth century. Until the 1870s it was quite a common sight to see even a big trans-Atlantic liner steaming along with a full spread of white canvas. Even all-steel, heavily armoured battleships carried sails. But in 1870 one of Britain's latest battleships, H.M.S. *Captain*, which had towering masts and heavy yards above her huge gun-turrets, capsized and sank in the Bay of Biscay with the loss of nearly all her crew. After that most builders tried to make ships safer, and such heavy weight aloft gradually disappeared.

The Great Days of Sail 1800-1870

At the beginning of the last century the most important sea-route in the world was that between Britain and India by way of the Cape of Good Hope. Britain ruled India through the great East India Company. Government officials, clerks, merchants, army officers and the families of all were always travelling to and fro. Cargoes of enormous value, including silk, spices, silver and precious stones, had to be carried regularly. So did all the world's supply of tea, which was then grown only in China. The tea thrown into Boston harbour during the celebrated tea party of 1773 had been carried there by East India Company ships. For the East India Company held a monopoly of all this vastly profitable trade, and no other ships were allowed to share it.

The East Indiamen, as these ships were called, were the finest merchant vessels afloat. They were built like battleships and were run like battleships with huge crews and haughty well-born officers – for an appointment in the Merchant Service, as they called it, was as much prized as a commission in the Royal Navy. And these ships, all heavily armed, could fight like battleships. In 1800 one chased and captured a French frigate, and in 1804 the China tea fleet put to flight a French battle squadron.

Yet as passenger ships these fine vessels left

100 Racing home with China tea, *Ariel* and *Taeping* still neck and neck in the English Channel after more than ninety days. *Taeping* won by twenty minutes.

much to be desired, at any rate by our modern standards. An army lieutenant would be lucky to have a camp bed or hammock in the 'tween-deck space, with a gun to sit on and a canvas screen to give him privacy. A wealthy merchant or high official might hire the captain's cabin, but he would have to supply his own furniture, including a bed! Only the meals were sumptuous, with whole barrels of wine to wash down the numerous courses. The company once had to issue an order that dinner, served at midday, should not last after five in the evening!

Also many of these ships were very slow. In some the captain would reduce sail at night in order to give himself and his passengers a comfortable sleep. Comfort and safety mattered; speed did not, for the East India Company had no competitors. A voyage to India and China and back might last two years.

But that sort of thing could not last for ever. The East India Company was becoming too rich and powerful. Other nations were demanding to be allowed to trade with India. More and more American ladies wanted China tea to drink and were angry that the East India Company's monopoly made it so expensive.

In 1832 the British Government took the first step by saying the East India Company could no longer run ships. Immediately other owners jumped into the trade and some fine, fast sailing passenger ships appeared on the Indian route. Built at Blackwall on the Thames and run like warships – though their gun-ports were mostly mere painted imitations – they were known as Blackwall frigates. For about thirty years they were the queens of the Indian Ocean, until the steamers of the P. & O. Line stole their trade from them.

Meanwhile the China tea trade remained mainly in the hands of the owners of the old-type East Indiamen – big lumbering ships scornfully called 'tea-wagons'. But in the New World the Americans were developing a very different kind of ship, the clipper.

America demanded speed. She first built fast sailing ships to beat the British warships during the War of Independence and the War of 1812. Then bigger ships were built on similar lines for long-distance ocean trading, and by the 1840s the real clipper had arrived. She was just in time to carry gold-hungry men to California for the great Gold Rush of 1849.

This brought a fantastic boom in ship-building. Suddenly every yard on the eastern

101   The fastest tea clipper ever? The *Thermopylae* carrying all possible sail. Her great rival was the *Cutty Sark* (see below).

side of the United States was building big fast ships, and even some carpentry yards where hitherto nothing had been built except chairs and tables. And as soon as they were built – some of hastily-cut unseasoned wood, some horribly unseaworthy – they were filled with

102   *Torrens*, Australian wool clipper and passenger ship. The famous author Joseph Conrad was once her first mate. Launched 1875, broken up 1910.

103   The famous *Cutty Sark*, tea and wool clipper. Sailed through the First World War as a Portuguese tramp. Was rescued, restored and preserved in drydock.

gold-hunters and sent off on the long, danger-ous voyage down to Cape Horn and north-wards to the wonderlands of California. Hundreds were never heard of again; but the best of them startled the world. Sailing ships had never before achieved such speeds. *Ninety days to 'Frisco!* some of them boasted, and that seemed incredible to most people for a voyage of 12,000 miles.

Captain 'Bully' Waterman was perhaps the most famous, or notorious, of all the hard-driving Yankee skippers who raced their ships round Cape Horn to California in gold-rush days. He could turn a slow ship into a record-breaker and convert a pack of land-lubbers into a crew of prime seamen in one voyage. Shipowners squabbled for his services and towns feted him; but his success went to his head and brought about his downfall.

He would shoot with a pistol at men on the yard to hurry them along. He once scalped his steward with a carving knife. He would fight with anybody, using any weapon from his fists to his prized sextant; but at the start of each voyage he took care to have the men's kit searched for weapons and always had the points broken off their sheath-knives.

In 1851, in command of the big clipper *Challenge*, he killed an old Italian seaman who could not work because his feet were frost-bitten. But that was only his worst crime of many during a hellish voyage. On arrival in San Francisco the tale of it caused a riot and Waterman had to give himself up to the police

to escape lynching. Then he used his dollars – for he was moderately rich by that time – to bribe judge and jury and secure an acquittal.

The affair had scared some commonsense into him, however, and he never dared go to sea again. He bought a farm in Solano County, California and died on it quietly enough in 1884.

Some of these wonderful ships took to running across the Pacific to China for a cargo of tea. From New York round the Horn to San Francisco, across to China, then home by way of the Indian Ocean and Cape of Good Hope – a round-the-world voyage of about 35,000 miles, yet they could be back in New York within ten months. Some of the old 'tea-wagons' took that time to sail from China to Britain!

But British owners did not really stir them-selves until the big Yankee clippers began bringing their cargoes of tea into London itself. Then there was such an outcry in Britain that soon British-built tea clippers were on the scene and for a while, in the 1850s, there was fierce Anglo-American competition and some hectic racing. In general the British tea clippers were smaller and handier than their big American rivals, for the latter had been built to withstand Cape Horn storms. In light winds and in the tricky waters of the China Sea the real tea clippers had the advantage. In a gale of wind with the open ocean before them the Yankees scored.

That was why big American clippers were used, even by British owners, when a new gold rush began to Australia in 1854. Once again everybody wanted to get to the treasure fields in a hurry and speed was all-important. But once again there was such a huge demand for ships of any kind that the crankiest old tub could get a full load of passengers who scarcely knew the difference between a clipper and a barge. And at the other end of the scale even the lordly Blackwall frigates left the Indian run to join in the scramble to Australia.

Soon after this, and almost suddenly, America lost interest in the racing clippers she had made so famous. The reason was that a railroad had been built across the continent. Nobody now would go to California by sea. And on the Atlantic, where American clippers had also been carrying thousands of passengers, steam liners had cut the crossing time from weeks to days.

But in the China tea trade the little British clippers were entering upon their great days. Every year they raced to be first home with the new season's tea and some of their names are still famous – *Thermopylae*, *Cutty Sark*, *Sir Lancelot*, *Ariel*, *Taeping* and the rest. So they raced on until 1869 when the opening of the

Suez Canal gave steamers an easier route than the long haul round the Cape of Good Hope. And then the clippers had to switch to the Australian wool trade, or had to cut down their beautiful towering rigs and become humble tramps.

How fast were the clippers? The American-built, British-owned *James Baines* once clocked twenty-one knots – the highest speed ever recorded by a sailing ship. In 1854 a similar ship, *Champion of the Seas*, *averaged* twenty knots for a whole day while running out to Australia. These were big ships, driving hard before a full gale, and by comparison the smaller tea clippers were much slower, having a maximum speed of perhaps fifteen or sixteen knots. Yet, oddly enough, it is the tea clipper *Thermopylae* – great rival of the famous *Cutty Sark* – which still holds the record for the fastest run from Britain to Australia. Twice she went out in sixty days, whereas the best run of the *James Baines*, of twice her size, was sixty-three days. Some of the later 'wind-jammers' got very near these figures, too. As late as 1933–4 the 3,000-ton German four-master *Padua* took only sixty-six days from Hamburg to South Australia. What has to be remembered, however, is that in the 1850s and 1860s these speeds were much, much faster than any steamer could achieve. In fact it was quite common for the mate of a clipper, when overtaking a steamer, to dangle a rope at the stern, jeeringly offering the labouring 'kettle' a tow!

105   Not warships, but East Indiamen coming home from China with tea. In 1804 they fought off a French battle squadron.

The Ocean-conquering Ship 1450-1750

Man generally succeeds in inventing what he needs when he needs it sufficiently. As our present civilisation has grown, with more people, more settled countries and more trade, so we have invented the steamship, the railroad, the motor car and air transport. But the very first thing which modern man had to acquire, long before all these, was the ocean-going sailing ship; because the ancient civilisations – of Egypt, Greece, Rome or even China – did not possess real ocean-going vessels at all.

The ocean-going sailing ship arrived just as abruptly as the ocean-going steamer, within a period of, say, fifty years. Columbus crossed the Atlantic for the first time in 1492; fifty years earlier he could not have done it, simply because no ship existed fit to make such a voyage.

Prince Henry the Navigator of Portugal must have most of the credit. He, leading the world, saw that the time had come for European man to learn more about the world. So he began by sending little ships out to explore the coast of Africa, in about 1420, and very soon

realised that these little ships were not good enough. Then he and his experts – designers, shipwrights and seamen – set about producing something better.

They began with the 'caravel', a small, half-open fishing or coastal trading craft with a single mast and a big triangular sail called 'lateen' – exactly the same as is used by Arab dhows to this day. This small vessel the Portuguese made larger, added one or two more masts, and decked in and added cabins. But she was still not really suitable for ocean sailing, so they borrowed ideas from northern Europe where the English, French and Scandinavian seamen had developed a tubbier, tougher kind of ship for their rough northern seas, with big square sails instead of the southern lateen kind.

The result was a ship like Columbus's *Santa*

50

107 A caravel of the fifteenth century. With such little ships Portuguese navigators explored the African coast for Prince Henry.

108 An early galleon or carrack of about 1500. With such ships Spain and Portugal ruled vast American and Indian empires.

109 A later Spanish galleon, much decorated. Most galleons of the sixteenth century had four masts, but later ships had only three.

Maria – big enough to carry crew, provisions and trading goods for a long period, high out of the water and broad enough to stay afloat in the roughest seas, yet quite handy to sail with her three masts, two with square sails and the third, the mizzen, carrying a lateen sail.

This was the kind of ship which all western nations adopted and improved upon from about 1490 onwards, and even the Chinese copied when the oceans were conquered and East met West. It was the kind of ship from which grew the great Spanish treasure galleons of the next century, and the fine English galleons with which Drake, Hawkins and the rest beat the Spanish Armada.

110 The ships of Columbus. The flagship *Santa Maria* is in the centre, the smaller *Pinta* on the right, the caravel *Nina* on left.

111 Drake's celebrated *Golden Hind*. In 1577–80 she sailed round the world via South America, California, China and Africa.

Amerigo Vespucci, the man who gave his name to America, went to sea in such a ship. He was an Italian clerk who settled in Spain and, after writing invoices for ships' stores and cargoes for some years, decided that he would like to go to sea himself. So in 1497 he joined some other adventurers and crossed the Atlantic to take a look at the wonderful new lands Christopher Columbus had just discovered.

Nobody knows just where he went on this or any of his subsequent voyages, for he was a bad navigator and a haphazard explorer and also a great liar. We know he was a liar because in the books he wrote afterwards he described voyages which must have taken him clean across both American continents and also deep into Antarctica! But he did make one important statement. The new lands, he said, were really

112   The *Great Harry* or *Harry Grâce à Dieu*,
King Henry VIII's super-battleship of 1514.
She rolled too heavily to be of much use at sea.

113   A battleship of 1638, the *Sovereign*
elaborately decorated. King Charles I buil
such ships with the hated Ship Money Tax

new – part of a vast hitherto unknown continent, and not part of Asia, of the East Indies, as Christopher Columbus was still insisting.

A great German map-maker, Martin Waldseemüller, took note of that and agreed. On his next map of the world, published in 1507, he called the new lands *America, the lands of Americus Vesputius*, which was the Latin form of the Italian clerk's name, Amerigo Vespucci. And poor Christopher Columbus, who was still calling *his* lands China and Japan, received no honour at all.

They made Amerigo Vespucci Chief Pilot of Spain after that; but, perhaps wisely, he went no more to sea.

Nor did it really change very much till the steamer came along to drive sail from the seas. Ships were built stronger as shipwrights became more skilful and had better tools. The old high forecastles and poops became smaller and hull design was improved. New sails were invented, such as triangular jibs and staysails to supplement the main square sails. But for more than two hundred years after Columbus practically all ships still carried the lateen mizzen sail, inherited from Prince Henry's caravels. Even Nelson's *Victory*, built in 1765, had a long lateen mizzen-yard, though probably she never set a lateen sail on it.

So it was the three-masted, square-rigged 'ship' rig which really conquered the oceans and made our modern civilisation possible. And it remained the most popular rig for big sailing vessels until they vanished from the oceans altogether.

114 Merchant shipping of about 1750. In the foreground is a Danish timber carrier, straight-sided and square-bowed for the stowage of big logs inside.

Round Ships and Long Ships

Very, very early in history, and perhaps before history began, man discovered that he needed two quite different kinds of ship or boat. He wanted one long and narrow which could be rowed easily with oars. He wanted one broad and tubby enough to carry cargo and remain afloat in choppy seas; but this one had to be sailed.

Nobody knows when man first discovered how to propel a boat with oars or paddles, nor when he first learnt to use the power of the wind. Ancient Egyptian and other pictures at least five thousand years old show both rowing and sailing boats. The Greeks who went to the siege of Troy a thousand years before Rome was thought of knew both the 'round' ship and the 'long' ship, as the two kinds were called.

Once these two kinds of ship had been developed, the round ship for cargo carrying and the long ship or rowing galley for war and other special purposes, they changed very little for hundreds and even thousands of years. The ships of Crete, which was the chief naval power in the Mediterranean four thousand years ago, were very like those of ancient Greece a thousand years later. The Romans improved upon them in detail, but basically they did not alter them. And long after the collapse of the Roman Empire men were building just the same kinds of ship for use in the Mediterranean. Not until man wanted to cross the great oceans was any serious attempt made to produce a new type of ship altogether.

Of course there were bound to be some differences. Men build ships for their own special purposes and with the materials available to them. In our own time Holland, for instance, has always specialised in shallow, flat-bottomed ships suited to its shallow coastal waters and estuaries. Around the coasts of Britain or France or Spain there are still quite distinct types of coastal and fishing craft specially suited to local conditions. In America the famous Newfoundland Banks fishing schooners were a type quite on their own.

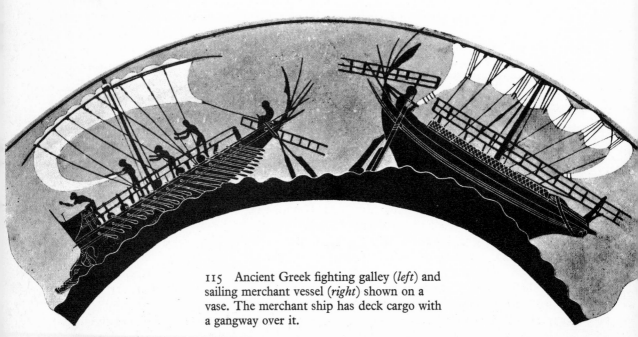

115 Ancient Greek fighting galley (*left*) and sailing merchant vessel (*right*) shown on a vase. The merchant ship has deck cargo with a gangway over it.

116 A Roman corn ship like the one in which St Paul was wrecked. She carried 250 tons of cargo and 270 passengers and crew.

In countries with plenty of big trees one might expect to find sturdy, well-built wooden ships. But in Egypt, where timber has always been scarce, ships were cleverly constructed of small pieces of wood laced and interlocked together, or even of long reeds tied in bundles.

We do not know much about the ordinary cargo-carriers, the 'round' ships, of the ancient world. They were so common, so ordinary and uninteresting to the people of that time that few artists bothered to illustrate them, or writers to mention them. Most people were far more proud of the warships of their time the fast oared 'long' ships, so these they wrote about and put into their sculptures and pictures on vases.

In general, however, we can say that they were very small, mostly not more than fifty feet long, built to carry perhaps ten or twenty tons of cargo. They would have nearly flat bottoms so that they could sit comfortably on most beaches; for we know that in ancient days seamen did not like sailing at night and often beached their ships at sunset. They would have only one mast with a single squaresail upon it,

until the Arabs came into the Mediterranean in about AD 600 and taught Europeans to use the lateen sail.

We do know that the Romans built bigger and better cargo ships, especially to carry corn from Egypt to Rome. The Roman corn ship in which St Paul was wrecked on Malta in AD 54 was about ninety feet long by twenty-seven feet broad, had a small foremast and sail in addition to her mainmast and mainsail, and could carry 250 tons of cargo besides some 270 passengers. But she was very slow and clumsy, and her skipper seemed terrified at the prospect of being caught at sea when winter came. You can read the full story in the Bible, Acts of the Apostles, chapter 27.

The 'long' ships, the rowing galleys, were nearly all fighting ships. To get speed and ease of rowing they were very narrow with fine lines and little draft of water. Nearly always they were rowed by slaves who were treated just like engines – fed, watered, but thrown away and replaced when they wore out. Above the human engine-room there was usually a long fighting-deck for the soldiers with their spears and bows and arrows. Right aft there might be an elaborate cabin or shelter for the

117 *St Nicholas Rebuking the Tempest.* But
the artist has shown us a typical Mediterranean ship of his own time, about 1300.

officers. Right forward, beneath the stem,
there would very likely be a metal-sheathed
wooden ram for smashing the hulls of enemy
galleys.

Some light galleys had only one 'bank' of
oars; but bigger vessels had two, three or even
five banks, and so were called biremes, triremes
or quinqueremes. These were not level banks
of oars and oarsmen one above the other, but
were staggered or overlapped in some way so
that the ship did not tower too far above the
water nor require the upper oars to be of an
impossible length. Whatever the arrangement,
the crowded oarsmen must have been exceed-
ingly uncomfortable, and there is plenty of
evidence that multi-banked galleys were not
very satisfactory. Galleys were used as vessels
of war in later years right down to the arrival
of the steam engine, but they were always
single-banked.

Most galleys carried a light mast and sail for
use in light following winds, but they were not
sailing ships in the usual sense of the term.
Their sails were purely auxiliary, and were
always put ashore when the galley went out to
fight. At such times she relied entirely upon
her human engines.

The Romans improved the galley too. But
they could not change her main style very
much, so they concentrated upon making her
more efficient in war. For instance, they
installed big stone-throwing catapults, and a
kind of flame-thrower, and a hooked gangway
for dropping on to an enemy's deck for the
soldiers to run across. And ashore they set up
rowing-machines for training galley crews.
But not even the Romans could make the
narrow, flimsy galley into a seaworthy craft.
More than once their entire navy was des-
troyed by a Mediterranean storm.

The galley could not be made really seaworthy, and therefore was never popular outside of the Mediterranean. The northern
nations of Europe preferred the tubby 'round'
ship with its ability to stay afloat in any
weather and its mast and sail for motive power.
So it was in the north – in Britain, Normandy,
Germany and the Baltic countries – that the
sailing ship came to be developed until
Portugal borrowed it for her ocean voyages.

In northern Europe even the warship was a
'round' ship. In fact during Norman times and
the Middle Ages there was no difference
between the cargo ship and the warship. When

warships were needed, any suitable merchant ships were hired or seized, had fighting 'castles' tacked on to them at bow and stern, were filled with soldiers and given a military captain and sent out to fight. Even against the Spanish Armada most of the English ships were lightly armed merchantmen, though most of the actual fighting was done by Queen Elizabeth's big galleons.

The sailing ship developed slowly, however. Through the Dark Ages of northern Europe, after the collapse of the Roman Empire, the big open oared-boat was the most common kind of craft. This was the kind of boat the Vikings used – broader and more seaworthy than a Mediterranean galley, but depending mainly on oars and using its single sail only in suitable weather.

The famous Viking 'longship', so often shown in pictures with its dragon's head at the prow and its rows of shields hung along its sides to protect the rowers, was in fact the Norseman's fighting ship. For more peaceful purposes, for trading and for moving his people, animals and household goods, he would

118 Ships of the Norman Conquest shown in the Bayeux Tapestry. Even horses were carried in them as well as sectional wooden castles.

have used a somewhat clumsier and less pretentious craft.

When William the Conqueror invaded England in 1066 his army, horses, supplies and portable wooden castles were carried in little ships very like the Viking craft, as we may see illustrated in the Bayeux Tapestry. But by this time, it seems, men were depending more upon sails. And as the years pass we find oars becoming more and more the auxiliary means of propulsion. At sea the ship always sailed; she used her oars only for manœuvring in harbour, to help the ship in turning, and so on – much as a modern sailing yacht uses her auxiliary motor.

Most probably the Vikings used their big single squaresails only with a light following wind. Their masts were always made to be lowered when not in use, and a mast made like that is not meant to be used in a gale. But in Norman times and later, masts were much stouter and were stepped into the ship's keel. They were meant for real sailing in any weather, with the wind from any direction.

For by that time seamen had learnt that by hauling one edge of the squaresail forward, and bracing it to the ship's bow, the ship could be sailed *across* the wind and not only with the wind right astern. So we see from old drawings

the appearance of a rope called a *bowline* for hauling the sail forward, and then the development of the spar projecting forward from the bows which we call the *bowsprit*. Ships shown on old coins, in the coats of arms and seals of ancient cities and on carvings, enable us to trace the slow change of the sailing ship through the centuries.

Ships became larger, too, as the world recovered from the chaos of the Dark Ages and trade increased. And as the ship grew bigger, so the old single squaresail became too big for a small crew to handle with safety. Therefore the next step was to divide the single sail into two, the mainsail and the topsail; or to give the ship two masts with one or two sails on each. Presently, too, we find the appearance of that little squaresail beneath the bowsprit, called the *spritsail*, which all square-rigged ships carried in Tudor times to help with their steering.

The main steering instrument was, of course, the rudder. In ancient times this had always been in the form of a steering oar held over one side of the stern. In Egypt and some other Mediterranean countries two such oars were used, one on each side of the stern. But in the north, in Viking times and later, only one oar was used, generally on the windward side of the vessel – the steering-side, or steer-board, from which we get our word *starboard*.

The Romans converted this steering oar into something like a modern rudder by securing it to the ship's side so that the helmsman had only to turn it instead of using it like an oar and strenuously exerting leverage on it. But the real rudder, as we know it, hung centrally on the stern and controlled from on deck by an arrangement of levers or wheel and chain, did not appear till 1300–50. At about the same time ships began to have square sterns, instead of the pointed or rounded form used by the ancient world and by the Vikings and Normans. A square stern, with a straight sternpost, made the hanging of a central rudder an easy matter.

It is a pity that we know very little about the development of the ship in other parts of the world during these early times. But we do know that Arab navigators regularly crossed the Indian Ocean from the Red Sea to India long before Vasco da Gama appeared in those waters with his 'new' ocean-going sailing ships. We know that Chinese goods somehow reached Africa, and that when Marco Polo and his uncles returned home from China in 1295 they travelled as passengers aboard a Chinese ship as far as Persia. Fortunately Marco Polo has

119 An Arab dhow of modern times, In just such ships Arab traders voyaged to India many centuries ago. The lateen rig is at least a thousand years old.

120 Portuguese lateen-rigged 'feluccas' of recent times. They are very like Columbus's caravel *Nina* – see 110 *on page* 51.

left us some description of the big Chinese ships of this period.

They had four masts, says the great traveller, with nine sails, and carried a crew of about 250 men. They had double-skinned hulls, of which the outer skin could be renewed when it became eaten by worm. Cabins for forty or more passengers could be erected on or below deck, while watertight bulkheads divided the hull into separate holds or compartments for safety. They were fastened with iron nails and coated outside with a kind of tar. They carried very large oars or sweeps to assist the sails.

Marco Polo was impressed because they were much bigger than the ships of his native Venice at that time. But from other things he says we may doubt whether they were real ocean-going vessels. On the whole they seem to have been giant, slow-moving coastal craft, always travelling with a fleet of smaller vessels in attendance. And Marco Polo's voyage to Persia lasted two years, while 600 people died from various causes on the way!

121 Norman warships, very like Viking ships, but with no oars shown. Note the form of 'crow's-nest' for a lookout man at the mast-top.

122 A modern Chinese junk with traditional matting sails plus a European-type jib. The junk is many centuries old.

123 Roman war galleys at sea. The picture is highly imaginative, the sails shown being of North European type of about 1800.

124 This 'royal' Chinese junk was sailed to England for the Great Exhibition of 1851, to advertise China tea. Its owner was a tea merchant.

In the Beginning

125 Noah building his Ark. Early artists portrayed such scenes in the setting of their own times. Here we see boatbuilding in the Middle Ages.

And so we arrive back at the very beginning of things, when man first felt the need to get afloat. Why did he? Probably for a variety of reasons, in various parts of the world. Perhaps he merely wanted to cross a river to explore its farther bank, or because some animal he was hunting swam across and so escaped. Or he may have seen how flotsam travelled down a river so much more easily than he could do overland upon his two legs. Or perhaps floods inundated his homeland and forced him to go afloat, as Noah was forced – and it is interesting to note that there are similar Great Flood tales in a dozen different primitive legends, in various parts of the world. Or, of course, he may have wanted the security from enemies or wild beasts of an island dwelling in some lake or marshland.

For whatever reason, right back in the dawn of time man began making boats, or using what was to hand in the way of fallen trees or other debris. He went afloat, almost certainly, before he had tools or skill to make anything. But when he acquired tools and skill he turned them to boat-building without loss of time. And it is interesting that in remote parts of the world primitive peoples are still making boats in much the same ways as our most distant ancestors used.

Much depends upon what material is to hand. Where there are trees men will scrape and burn part of the wood away to make dugout canoes, as in parts of Africa, in the Amazon forests or in Borneo. Where there are long, tough reeds they may be tied in bundles to form a rough boat as is still done in parts of the Sudan, and as was done in ancient Egypt thousands of years ago. Or they may be woven together and pitched to make basket boats like the Welsh coracle. Julius Caesar took British coracle-makers with him on the march, to make boats for crossing rivers.

The Eskimo makes his *kayak* out of animal skins stretched over light bentwood frames, as his ancestors did centuries ago; but the Red Indian preferred to use the thin bark of birch trees for the covering skin. The early inhabitants of Peru made rafts of the feather-light balsa trees, and the famous *Kontiki* of a

60

126 A model of the famous *Kontiki* raft upon which Norwegian scientists in 1947 followed the route of South Sea islanders of a thousand years earlier.

127 Welshmen with their basketwork coracles on their backs. Julius Caesar used similar boats to ferry his soldiers across British Rivers.

few years ago was built in the same way. Boats may still be seen on the Tigris and Euphrates which are merely inflated animal skins – the principle we now use for inflatable rubber dinghies. In India boats are sometimes made of interwoven large leaves, as no doubt they were made when man had scarcely entered the Stone Age.

Man has been making boats ever since he could be called man – perhaps even before he began making houses or cooking his food. He will go on making boats till the end of time because – well, because, as Water Rat says in *The Wind in the Willows*. 'There is *nothing*, absolutely nothing, half so much worth doing as simply messing about in boats.'

128 Viking ship – found in a grave and preserved at Oslo, Norway. Richly carved, long, light and fast, perhaps a chieftain's pleasure yacht.

Contents

Acknowledgements

The author and publishers acknowledge their grateful thanks to the owners for permission to use the copyright illustrations listed below:

To Adriatica S.P.A. di Navigazione, for: 30 and 31

To Ashmolean Museum, Oxford, for: 117

To Beken & Son, for: 43, 44 and 45

To Coast Lines Ltd, for: 21

To J. Combier, for: 118

To Cunard Line, for: 11, 42, 46, 47 and 49

To French Line, C.G.T., for: 41

To Frost & Reed Ltd, for: 101

To Gas Council, for: 29

To Hawthorn Leslie, for: 20

To Hovertravel Ltd, for: 6

To Humble Oil & Refining Co, for: 2

To *Illustrated London News*, for: 37

To Imperial War Museum, for: 5 and 57

To Paul Kirby, for: 119

To Mastboom Vliegbedrijf, N.V., for: 33

To Ministry of Defence, Crown Copyright Reserved, for: 50 and 51

To National Maritime Museum, for: Title page, 9, 10, 58, 59, 60, 61, 63, 64, 66, 67, 68, 69, 73, 75, 76, 78, 80, 81, 82, 83, 84, 85, 86, 87, 88, 90, 91, 92, 93, 95, 96, 97, 98, 99, 102, 103, 104, 105, 106, 112, 113, 114 and 129

To Novosti Press Agency, for: 8

To Port of London Authority, for: 12, 13, 14, 15, 16, 17, 18, 19, 28 and 48

To Press Association, for: 70 and 77

To Radio Times Hulton Picture Library, for: 4, 23, 26, 34, 35, 36, 55, 62, 65, 71, 72, 79, 89, 94, 100, 107, 108, 109, 110, 111, 120, 121, 122, 123, 124, 125, 126 and 127

To Ruston & Hornsby Ltd, for: 32

To Science Museum, for: 115

To Shell Photographic Service, for: 22, 25 and 27

To Shipping World, for: 1

To Skyfotos, for: 24

To Union-Castle Line, for: 40

To United States Line, for: 38 and 39

To University of Oldsaksamling, for: 128

To U.S. Navy, for: 3, 52, 53, 54 and 56

Index

129 In 1740–4 Commodore Anson repeated Drake's feat of sailing round the world and capturing rich Spanish treasure. Here his *Centurion* is fighting the big galleon *Cobadonga*.

Printed in Great Britain by Jarrold & Sons Ltd, Norwich